3/10

To Nelson

Text copyright © 2004 by Harriet Ziefert
Illustrations copyright © 2004 by Simms Taback
All rights reserved. CIP Data is available.
Published in the United States 2004 by
🍎 Blue Apple Books
515 Valley Street, Maplewood, N.J. 07040
www.blueapplebooks.com
Distributed in the U.S. by Chronicle Books
First Edition
Printed in China
ISBN 1-59354-035-3
3 5 7 9 10 8 6 4 2

Simms Taback's Big Book of Words

Blue Apple Books

Playthings

airplane

teddy bear

paint box

boat

horn

book

telephone

RRRRRRING   RRING

crayon

tambourine

doll

tools

ball

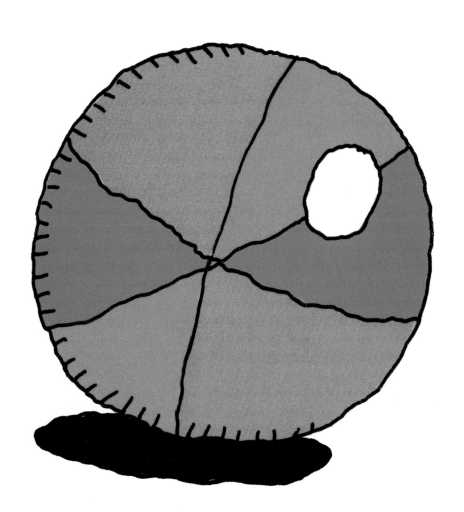

pail and shovel

car

blocks

mixing bowl

measuring cup
and spoons

tricycle

drum

keys

dump truck

Clothing

bib

T-shirt

overalls

daddy's shoes

mommy's hat

socks

shoes

boots

raincoat

bathing suits

sunglasses

snowsuit

sweater

jacket

dress

scarf

mittens

jeans

shirt

bathrobe

pajamas

Food

orange

banana

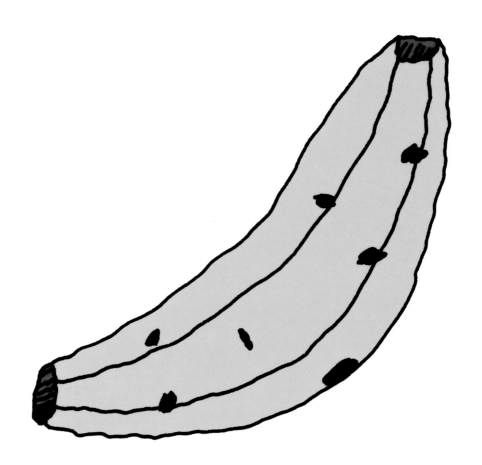

watermelon

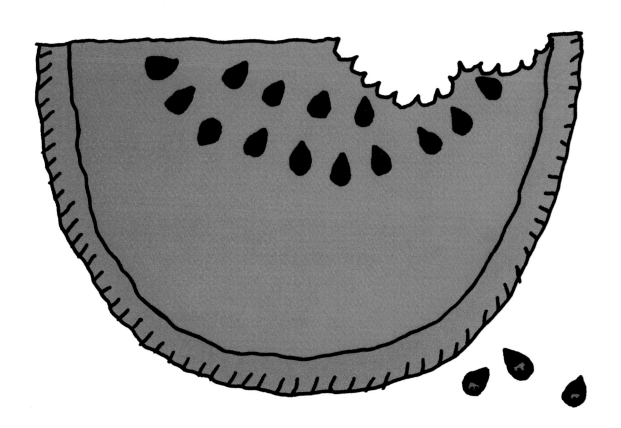

cereal

corn

popcorn

kitty's milk

baby's milk

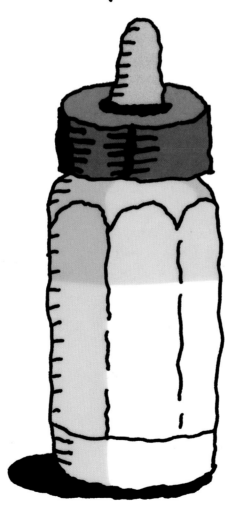

carrots

tomato

peanut butter and jelly

Sandwich

yogurt

strawberries

pretzel

cake

bread

cheese

hot dog

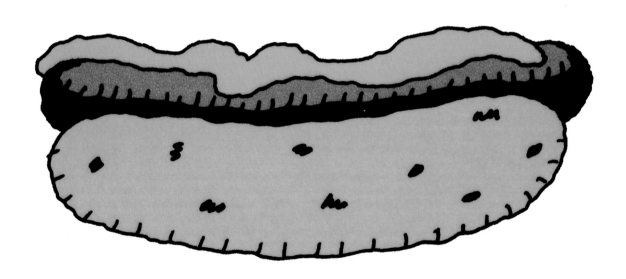

ice cream

Animals

cat

goose

rooster

grasshopper

ladybug

frog

skunk

mouse

yak

parrot

flamingo

sheep

pig

elephant

zebra

Snake

fish

duck

rabbit

bear

Owl